W9-ATE-418

THE
MAD
ADVENTURES OF
CAPTAIN KLUTZ

Illustrated by Don Martin

Written by Dick DeBartolo, Phil Hahn, Jack
Hanrahan and Don Martin. Edited by Nick Meglin.

WARNER BOOKS

A Warner Communications Company

**Warner Books, Inc.,
666 Fifth Avenue,
New York, N.Y. 10103**

W A Warner Communications Company

Printed in the United States of America

First Printing: October, 1974

Reissued: October, 1980

14   13   12   11

PROLOGUE

Not too many years ago, in a busy hospital
in the heart of teeming Megalopolis, a baby
was born. A baby marked even then
as different from the crowd . . .

In many ways, young Ringo Fonebone's
development was like that of any
other red-blooded American youth.
He slept . . . .

He ate . . . .

He learned to walk . . . .

But in one peculiar way, little Ringo was different. He spurned childish fairy tales and nursery rhymes for more **stimulating** reading matter . . . Namely, **comic books.**

Eventually, Ringo's specialized interests
led to a falling out with his parents . . .

It soon became apparent that Ringo was ill-equipped to cope with the outside world . . .

13

Assessing the situation carefully, Ringo did the only thing a man in his position could do . . . **He gave up!**

So much for a life of **heartbreak** and **shattered dreams!** I'm a **disgrace** to my **family,** my **friends, myself, Wonder Woman** . . . Oh, the **shame** of it all!!

16

RiP

KLOON

17

TONG

18

19

SPLOOF

22

23

24

25

And now...

CAPTAIN KLUTZ

faces one of the all time
fiendish criminals in one of the
strangest cases on record!

(RCA Victor LP 7899-67 Stereo & Mono)

It all began one night last June. I was having a **terrible** nightmare. I dreamt I was in some two bit room of a sleazy hotel. Chunks of the ancient plaster kept falling on me, and **cockroaches** climbed the wall . . .

Luckily, the phone rang to end my nightmare.
What a **relief** it was to **wake up!**

29

I knew there was only **one person** in all the
world with a voice like that! . . . **SISSYMAN!** If my
hunch was right, he was calling from his
secret hide-out, somewhere
in his **mother's house!**

30

Whenever he called me it meant he was going to **strike again** somewhere in the teeming metropolis. I **sprang** into action! It was Ringo Fonebone who answered the phone, but it was **CAPTAIN KLUTZ** who leaped out of the window!

. . . and onto the **fire escape!** Then I carefully walked down the 14 floors to the street. The building used to have a 15th floor but that's another story.

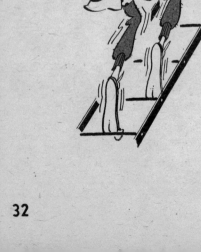

33

35

36

37

A LITTLE LATER AT THE MUSEUM

43

CLANK!

EARLY
AMERICAN
BEAR
TRAP.

45

Perhaps I should go to the Sissy's hide-out **alone!** If you don't hear from me in an hour, come and get me! The address is 411 Secret Hide-away Lane!
Fine! If I find out anything further here I'll call you on the **Klutz phone!**
It won't do you any good—I have an **unlisted number.**

49

50

51

52

53

54

55

56

57

I immediately leaped out of the window! Luckily, Sissyman's room was on the **ground** floor. It used to be on the **second** floor but that **too** is another story. My trusty Klutz-scooter was there and waiting!

Klutz!! Captain **Klutz!!** This is **police chief O'Freenbean!!!**

Of **course** you can hear me loud and clear, you **idiot!! Listen!!** Sissyman has just knocked over the First National Bank and is headed for the **Acme jewelry store** on **Main** Street! You better get over there **quick!!!**

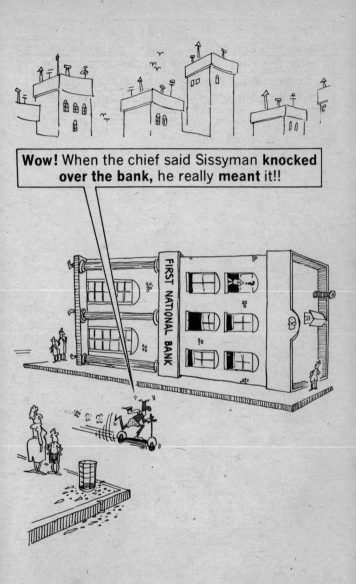

61

66

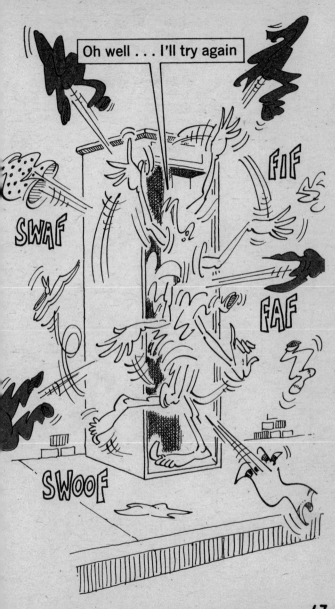

67

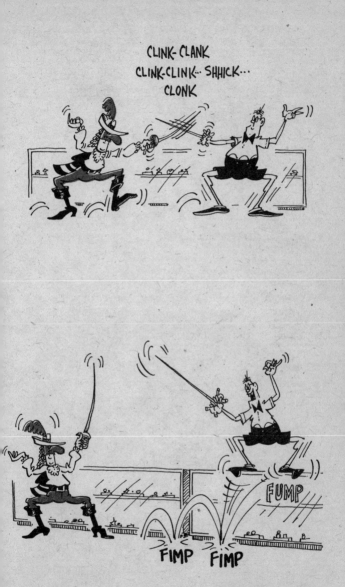

FIMP FIMP

KSSSH

FUMP

73

75

77

CAPTAIN KLUTZ

IN

THE

MESSAGE

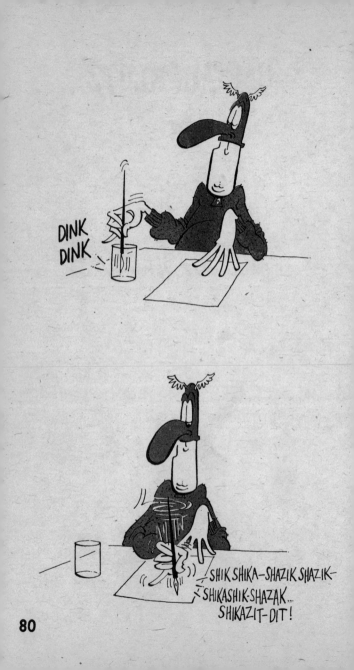

80

81

83

CAPTAIN KLUTZ

IN THE CASE
OF

CHICKEN
SOUP

(A call on the Klutzphone can only mean **one thing: dire emergency!**) Hello! Dire emergency? Captain **Klutz** speaking!

It's just me, Captain . . . Mrs. Hackleshmackle from downstairs. While you're downtown for the Granny Santini presentation, would you please get me a **50-pound bag of quick-setting pectin?** It's canning time, And I'm putting up a few jars of my famous pickled peppered pectined pigs feet for the High Holy Days.

I'd be delighted Mrs. Hackleshmackle.

89

91

Gad! A veritable **Zombie sweat shop!** **Someone's** making **use** of all the poor derelicts that Granny Santini has been trying to rehabilitate! I must warn her that all her **good work** has gone for **naught!!**

HOOKED RUG DEPT.

WICKER BASKET DEPT.

INDIAN POTTERY DEPT.

93

94

97

POINK

IS THIS THE END OF CAPTAIN KLUTZ?

100

101

105

106

The doctors say the effects of the drugged soup will wear off in a few days, and the Zombie derelicts will revert to their normal state of lovable worthlessness. So, once again, Klutz, our fair city **owes you its heart!**

That's all very well, chief, but I'll settle for **cash.**

THIS IS A RAIDED PREMISES

CAPTAIN KLUTZ

ON THE ELEVATOR

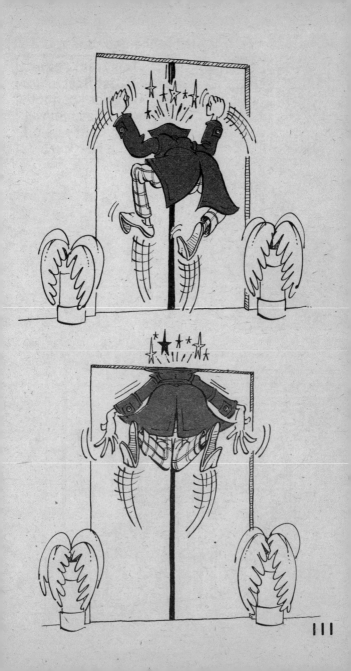

INTRODUCTION

114

115

And so, dear reader, now that we've got you
built up to fever pitch . . . we will begin
the next hair-raising episode entitled . . .

CAPTAIN KLUTZ

MEETS

GORGONZOLA

the crawling, hideous monster who lives only to terrorize and kill!

(Adapted very freely from "The Sound Of Music")

It all began as I was sleeping in
my new airy apartment, when
the sounds of panic awakened me . . .

Help! Help!

In a **flash** I was ready to face any danger that existed! For **I,** as you probably have **guessed** by now, am **Captain Klutz!!!**

Help! Eek!

We're being attacked by a **spider!!!**

PLOIP

121

With my Super-vision, I ran my eyes over the thing. There was no doubt about it—it was the dreaded monster, **GORGONZOLA!!** I acted as quick as I could and used my **Super-voice** . . .

122

123

I only screamed because I was caught off guard! Now that I had my **full** senses, I did the only logical thing I could . . . I **passed out!** When I awoke Chief O'Freenbean was standing over me . . .

Klutz! Klutz! Wake up!! What **happened?!!?**

The spider was so bored he walked away!

Drat! We'll **never** find him now! He'll hide until he's ready to **strike again!**
Not so, chief! I happen to have some electronic tracking equipment **in my cape!** Footprint detector . . . Color radar . . . Enemy decoder . . . Magnetic blit . . . Two-way plebney light . . .

133

135

137

138

141

143

CAPTAIN KLUTZ
MEETS
MERVIN
THE
MAD
BOMBER

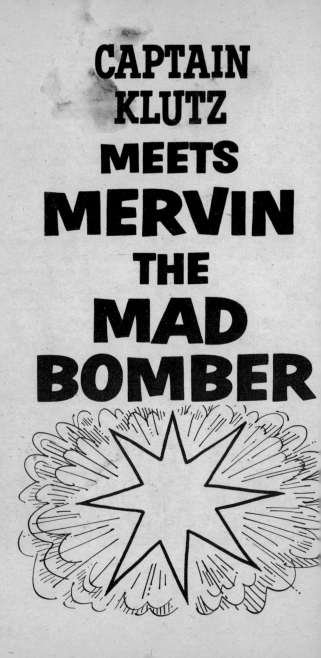

This is the city, sleeping tranquilly beneath a downy blanket of fresh fallen soot. As dawn breaks, alarm clocks all over town are awakening masses of simple folk who are blissfully unaware that this is not just another day . . . this is a day that terror will grip the hearts of—but let us not get ahead of our story. Let us turn instead to the simplest folk of all . . . a man known to his neighbors as "that little creep upstairs" . . . **Ringo Fonebone,** as he is awakened by **his** alarm clock . . .

147

149

150

152

153

154

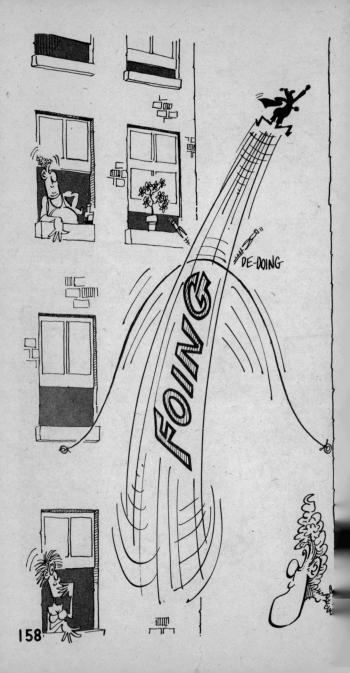

FOING

DE-DOING

161

KLUTZ'S

CHARCOAL
BRIQUETTES

PHAK!

171

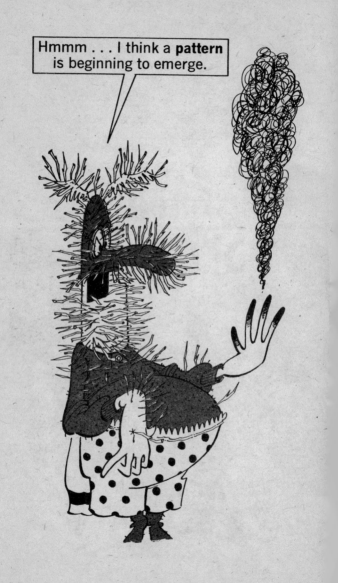

174

177

179

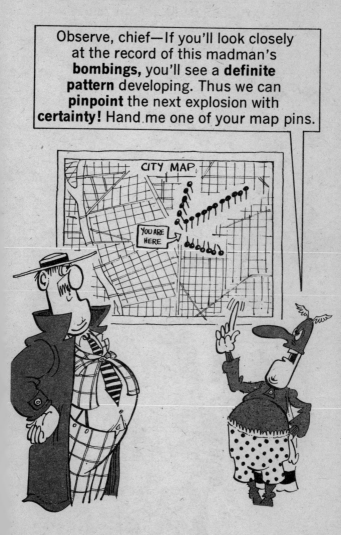

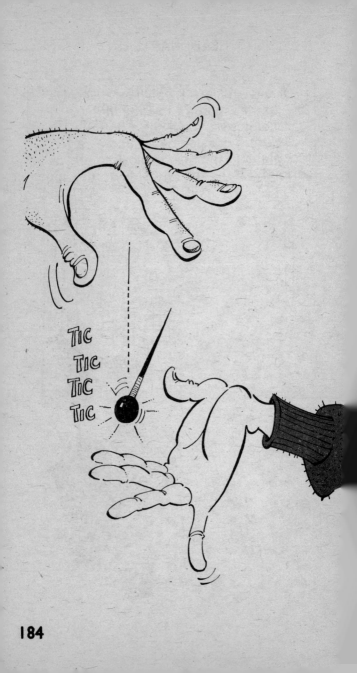

TIC
TIC
TIC
TIC

187

189

192